Yellow Bear GOES TO CATHOLIC SCHOOL

Written By: Carol Bryden and Dianne Lloyd
Illustrated By: Jeremy Bruneel

Published 2008 by St. Clair Catholic District School Board
420 Creek Street Wallaceburg, ON N8A 4C4

Then I heard the voice of
the Lord saying "Whom shall
I send? Who will go for us?"
"Here I am," I said, "send me!"
— Isaiah 6:8

Thanks to my friends Jan, Roelof, Marlene, Glenn, Wendy, Tammie, Ray and Arlene who help me think outside of the box... and my husband Hec and daughter Devon who help me stay focused on my beliefs.

– Dianne

Thank you to my family who inspire and support me in all that I do... and to my parents for choosing Catholic Education – it made all the difference.

– Carol

For my best friend and wife, Ann, for her never ending love and support, for my wonderful parents, all my family and friends. And a special thanks to Chris Kehoe.

– Jeremy

The authors and illustrator wish to thank the St. Clair Catholic District School Board and particularly the Catholic Education Coalition for their support of this project; and Todd Lozon for his wit, wisdom, and tireless support.

Yellow Bear sat on the toy box watching Mika get ready.
It was the first day of kindergarten and Yellow Bear was nervous.
What would Mika do without him?

He had always taken care of her.
Who would take care of Mika when she was at school?
Yellow Bear had an idea! He would go to school, too!

“Will you stay with me at school today?” Mika asked.
“No,” said Mom. “I must go back home with Devon. But remember Mika, Jesus will be with you all day. He is there in everyone you meet.”

Mika stayed close to her Mother. They passed St. Joseph Church.
“That’s where Devon was baptized!” announced Mika. “You too,” answered Mom.
They saw Father Todd. He waved and called “Good Morning!” to Mika.

In the playground, Yellow Bear saw the teachers helping the children.
Was Jesus in these teachers? He wondered.

Mika met a friend from her street. When she put down her backpack to play hopscotch, Yellow Bear nearly fell out of his hiding place!

After Mika kissed her mother good-bye, she felt a little sad. But when a girl with long braids asked to stand beside her, she felt much better. Mika remembered what Mother had said about Jesus.

The children walked inside with Miss Tang the kindergarten teacher. Yellow Bear saw a statue of St. Joseph in the hallway. It was just like the one at church.

Inside the classroom, Yellow Bear saw a lot of books. There were places to paint, blocks to build houses, trucks in a sand box and some boats floating in a big tub of water. "Wow," Yellow Bear thought, "this is going to be fun!"

Miss Tang showed the children the chalkboard. On it, she had printed the names of all the children. Yellow Bear looked for Mika's name, but he could only read the letter M and there were four names that started with M. Yellow Bear hoped he would learn to read, too.

ALL GOD'S
Ann
Aidan
Bonnie
Carlos
Chris
Glenn
Ji-Min
Macy
MiKa
Roelof

The children sat on the carpet in front of a beautiful table. On it was a picture of Jesus, a bible and a rosary. Miss Tang lifted the bible from the table and showed the children how to make the Sign of the Cross. Then she read them a story about how Jesus loved children. The story made Yellow Bear feel better.

When the story was finished,
the children made a leaf hat
with coloured paper, scissors,
glue and glitter.

Yellow Bear's tummy growled.
He was hungry! Miss Tang must
have heard it because she told the
children it was time to eat lunch.
They took turns washing their hands
and said a prayer together to thank
God for the food.

Now it was playtime. Miss Tang helped Mika tie her shoe and helped a boy zip up his coat. Yellow Bear watched.

He tried to squeeze out of the backpack, but he had to stay behind. He could hear the children playing in the yard. Was Mika OK? Was she all alone in the playground? Yellow Bear thought some more about what Mother had said.

Yellow Bear couldn't wait to see Mika when recess was over! She was laughing and holding hands with her new friend, a girl with red curls.

One of the boys had fallen playing hopscotch, so Miss Tang washed his knee, put a band-aid on it and gave him a hug.

ABC
123

Walter

The children put on their running shoes. On their way to the gym, they passed Mr. Walter, who was polishing the floor. He had a friendly smile. He waved and told them to have fun.

When they came back, Mika was giggling.

The children went outside to the Peace Garden and Miss Tang began reading them a story. Yellow Bear looked up. Father Todd had come to visit. Yellow Bear liked Father Todd. He finished reading the story to the children and then told them a funny 'knock-knock' joke. Even Miss Tang laughed!

It was time to go home. Miss Tang gave the children a letter for their parents. Mika squished the letter into her backpack, on top of Yellow Bear's head.

Mother was waiting with a big hug. Mika couldn't wait to tell her about her first day of Kindergarten and all of her new friends.

Mika took Yellow Bear out of her backpack and put him on her bed. He snuggled into the pillow and thought about all of the people at school. He knew that Mika would be safe and happy at St. Joseph Catholic School and that Jesus would be with her every day.

Tomorrow Mika would go to school all by herself and Yellow Bear would stay home and have a long, long, long nap.

It is our belief that parents desire a strong moral and faith-filled environment for their children, and that Catholic schools can provide such an environment through:

- a strong commitment to academic excellence,
- a safe and nurturing school environment,
- daily, meaningful faith experiences for students,
- a moral framework to guide student activity,
- integration of Gospel Values into the fabric of the student's day,
- a focus on the importance of the family and
- a curriculum which emphasizes social responsibility and stewardship.

The following activities may help you prepare your child for their first school experience.

Page 6 and 7
Ask your child about his feelings as he prepares to begin school. Explain your feelings to him. Talk about other times when you or your child have been nervous or afraid when beginning something for the first time. Use the picture to identify objects in Mika's room that make her feel safe and happy, then identify familiar objects in your home that provide a measure of safety and comfort for your child.

Page 8 and 9
Explore the picture with your child. Have her talk about going to school; walking with a parent or older sibling; traveling on a school bus; riding with a friend or neighbour. Talk about safety and what to do in an emergency. Explain to your child what Mother meant when she told Mika that Jesus would be there in everyone she met. Ask your child to identify qualities in people she knows that are like Jesus. Look at the picture of the church. Compare it to your parish church. Identify the priests working in your parish. Discuss your child's baptism. This is a good time to look at some photographs, if they are available.

Page 10 and 11
Discuss the playground at the school. If possible, take your child to the school and walk around to familiarize your child with the area. Talk about the activities children may be doing in the playground. Explain that the teachers are in the playground to watch over and protect all of the children. Discuss the things a teacher might do that would remind your child of Jesus. Talk about Yellow Bear and his interest in the activities.

Page 12 and 13
Talk with your child about his feelings when he is apart from you. What does your child do to feel better? If you know, explain to the child who the teacher may be. If the child has not met the teacher, talk about what he/she may look like. Explore the picture of St. Joseph. Ask your child to identify the statues or pictures at your parish church. You may wish to take your child to visit the church and identify some of the artefacts there.

Page 14 and 15
Explore the picture and identify the activities that can take place in the classroom. Ask your child to tell you which activities interest her most. Discuss the activities your child is looking forward to doing in kindergarten.

Page 16 and 17
Point out the chalkboard with the names of the children. Read the names to your child and ask if she knows anyone with those names. List the names of friends and family, including the child's name, and fasten it to the wall or refrigerator. This will remind your child that all children will meet old friends and make new ones at school. Have your child practice finding her name on the list. Discuss the books that your child likes to read at home.